hen

mice

lizards

butterflies

sunbirds

crickets

baby bullfrogs

spoonbills

starlings

For John and Milo

The children featured in this book are from the Luo tribe of south-west Kenya.

*The wild creatures are the Citrus Swallowtail (butterfly), Striped Grass Mouse,
Yellow-headed Dwarf Gecko, Beautiful Sunbird, Armoured Ground Cricket,
(young) African Bullfrog, African Spoonbill and Superb Starling.*

*The author would like to thank everyone who helped her research this book,
in particular Joseph Ngetich from the Agricultural Office of the Kenya High Commission.*

Text and illustrations copyright © 2002 Eileen Browne
Dual Language copyright © 2003 Mantra Lingua
This edition published 2003
Published by arrangement with Walker Books Limited
London SE11 5HJ

British Library Cataloguing in Publication Data:
a catalogue record for this book is available from the British Library.

Published by
Mantra Lingua
5 Alexandra Grove, London N12 8NU
www.mantralingua.com

A Galinha da Handa

Handa's Hen

Eileen Browne

mantra

A Avó da Handa tinha uma galinha preta.
O nome dela era Mondi – e todas as manhãs,
a Handa dava o pequeno-almoço à Mondi.

Handa's grandma had one black hen.
Her name was Mondi - and every morning
Handa gave Mondi her breakfast.

Um dia, a Mondi não veio buscar a sua comida.
"Avó!", chamou a Handa. "Vês a Mondi?"
"Não", respondeu a Avó. "Mas vejo a tua amiga."
"Akeyo!", exclamou a Handa. "Ajuda-me a encontrar a Mondi."

One day, Mondi didn't come for her food. "Grandma!" called Handa. "Can you see Mondi?"
"No," said Grandma. "But I can see your friend."
"Akeyo!" said Handa. "Help me find Mondi."

A Handa e a Akeyo procuraram à volta do galinheiro.
"Olha! Duas borboletas esvoaçantes", disse a Akeyo.
"Mas, onde está a Mondi?", perguntou a Handa.

Handa and Akeyo hunted round the hen house.
"Look! Two fluttery butterflies," said Akeyo.
"But where's Mondi?" said Handa.

Espreitaram por debaixo de um depósito de cereais.
"Chiu! Três ratos listados", disse a Akeyo.
"Mas, onde está a Mondi?", perguntou a Handa.

They peered under a grain store.
"Shh! Three stripy mice," said Akeyo.
"But where's Mondi?" said Handa.

Espreitaram por detrás de uns potes de barro.
"Vejo quatro lagartixas", disse a Akeyo.
"Mas, onde está a Mondi?", perguntou a Handa.

They peeped behind some clay pots.
"I can see four little lizards," said Akeyo.
"But where's Mondi?" said Handa.

Procuraram à volta das árvores em flor.
"Cinco belos pássaros", disse a Akeyo.
"Mas, onde está a Mondi?", perguntou a Handa.

They searched round some flowering trees.
"Five beautiful sunbirds," said Akeyo.
"But where's Mondi?" said Handa.

Olharam para a vasta erva ondulante.
"Seis grilos saltitantes!", disse a Akeyo. "Vamos apanhá-los."
"Quero encontrar a Mondi", disse a Handa.

They looked in the long, waving grass.
"Six jumpy crickets!" said Akeyo. "Let's catch them."
"I want to find Mondi," said Handa.

Desceram até ao poço de água.
"Rãs bebés", disse a Akeyo. "São sete!"

They went all the way down to the water hole.
"Baby bullfrogs," said Akeyo. "There are seven!"

"Mas onde está … Oh! Olha! Pegadas!", disse a Handa.
Seguiram as pegadas e descobriram …

"But where's … oh look! Footprints!" said Handa.
They followed the footprints and found …

"São apenas colhereiros", disse a Handa. "Sete … não, oito."
"Mas onde, oh onde está a Mondi?"

"Only spoonbills," said Handa. "Seven … no, eight.
But where, oh where is Mondi?"

"Espero que não tenha sido engolida por um colhereiro' –
Ou comida por um leão", disse a Akeyo.

"I hope she hasn't been swallowed by a spoonbill -
or eaten by a lion," said Akeyo.

Sentindo-se tristes, iniciaram o caminho de volta para a casa da Avó.
"Nove reluzentes estorninhos - além!", exclamou a Akeyo.

Feeling sad, they went back towards Grandma's.
"Nine shiny starlings - over there!" said Akeyo.

"Escuta", disse a Handa. ^{piu}piu "O que é isto?"
^{piu}piu ^{piu}piu ^{piu}piu ^{piu}piu
"Vem debaixo daquele arbusto – vamos espreitar?"

"Listen," said Handa. $^{cheep}cheep$ "What's that?"
cheep   cheep   cheep   cheep
cheep   cheep   cheep   cheep
"It's coming from under that bush. Shall we peep?"

A Handa, a Akeyo, a Mondi e os dez pintainhos

Handa, Akeyo, Mondi and ten chicks

numa correria, apressaram-se para a casa da Avó ...

hurried and scurried and skipped back to Grandma's ...

onde todas tomaram um pequeno-almoço tardio.

where they all had a very late breakfast.

hen

mice

lizards

butterflies

sunbirds

crickets

baby bullfrogs

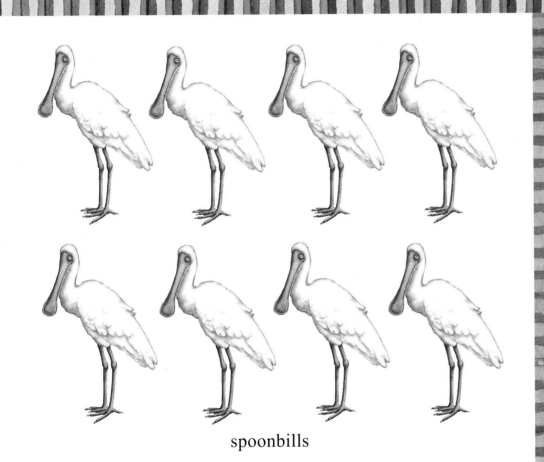

spoonbills

starlings

chicks